First paperback edition July 2021

Illustrations by Virvalle Carvallo

www.treindeer.com

ISBN: 978-0-578-97202-2

To my amazing son and daughter, Jackson & Arya.
You are loved more than you can ever imagine.

Treindeer

Hi! I'm Jackson and this is my sister Arya. We train reindeer at the North Pole and we really need your help.

Everyone has heard of Santa's famous reindeer. There's Dasher, Dancer, Prancer and Vixen. And of course, Rudolph!!

But did you know Santa has a 'B' Team of reindeer? These special reindeer assist Santa and his famous reindeer. They also solve problems and help the people of the North Pole and beyond! They are called Treindeer.

Since there are so many baby reindeer, only the most well-trained ones can become a part of the elite Treindeer. Santa needs you to help us train them to be ready for the North Pole!

In this book, Arya and I will teach you how to become a great trainer. After you complete the book, you'll get an official Treindeer certificate to show that you are a trainer, just like Arya and I! You can even get your very own Treindeer online too!

We have three awesome Treindeer who help us
and they are so excited to help you, too!

Marshmallow

is athletic, strong and confident.

He is a great leader with positive
energy, which allows him to
inspire others to become better.

Jules

is smart, assertive and courageous.

She's an excellent swimmer who always knows just what to do.

She helps Treindeer when they get into sticky situations.

Taco

is silly and fun to be around.

He is an extrovert that always plays jokes! Everyone loves him.

He is also lightning fast and wins every race in the reindeer games!

Now it's time to prepare for training!
Train your Treindeer in 3 areas:

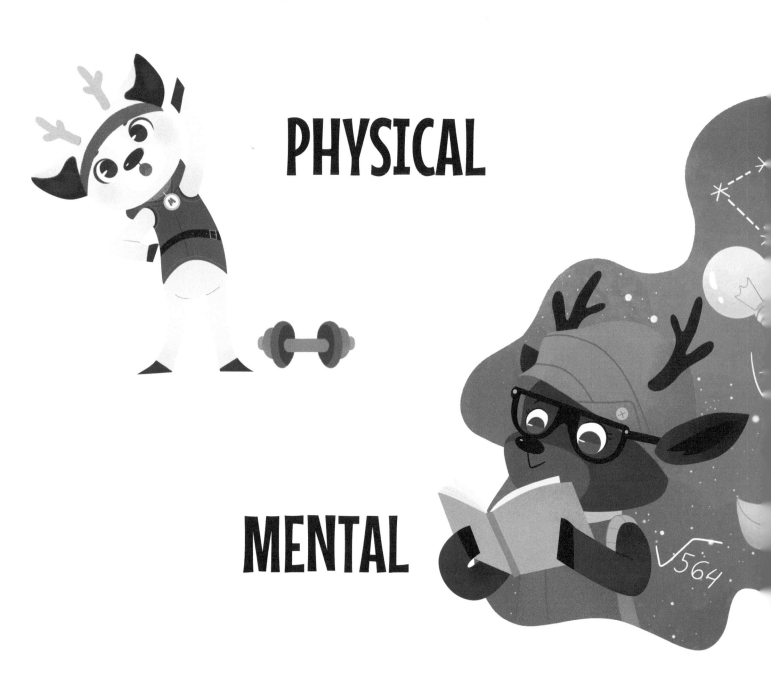

PHYSICAL

MENTAL

SILLINESS

1. PHYSICAL

Treindeer have a lot to do, so they have to be in tip-top shape! Here are some exercises for you to learn to help prepare your future Treindeer.

a. Jumping Jacks -
builds respiratory and control over the body

b. Bear Crawls -
builds strength in arms, shoulders and chest

c. Bunny Jumps -
builds strength in legs

d. Duck Walks. -
builds strength and
balance in legs

Who knew exercises could be silly!

Parents: Please make sure that your little ones are doing these exercises correctly to get the very most out of them.

Yoga helps build focus, strength and confidence. Follow along with Marshmallow to learn these fun poses that Treindeer always have a blast doing:

a.Downward dog

b.Upward dog

c.Tree

d.Bridge

f.Dancer's Pose

e.Child's Pose

g.Warrior 2 Pose

h.Happy Baby

2. MENTAL

Treindeer need to be their best for Santa, the elves and others. Here are some things that are important for both you and the Treindeer.

Tell the Truth. It helps Treindeer make friends easier and become more reliable and happy.

1 2 3...

Rock, Paper scissors!

Play with Friends. It's so much fun playing with friends! They help develop your personality and always make you laugh.

Display Courage. Courage is doing something hard or scary. It means we don't let the scary or hard things prevent us from doing something new, or even even what's right.

Be Creative. Creativity is super helpful for your Treindeer as it helps them solve tough problems!

Learn. Learning helps you become smarter, which is superhero strength. This is how you achieve your dreams.

Give love!. By showing love to everyone around, you make others feel important.

Have Confidence. Confidence is knowing you can do something. If what you do doesn't work, have the confidence to try again! Treindeer need to be confident because they never know what's in store for them at the North Pole!

Always Clean. It can get messy at the North Pole with all the snow, reindeer and presents. Tidying up keeps things organized.

Be happy. Being happy is a super important Treindeer strength that helps them feel good, loved and develop courage.

Listen to Parent(s). Treindeer need wisdom, guidance and help. Just like yours, their parents are the best teachers! Parents help keep you from making mistakes. They can even help you do things better!

3. SILLINESS

Our Treindeer love to be silly. Here are some fun games for you to practice being silly!

Hide-n-seek - Your mother, father, brother or sister hides and you find them.

Taco Says - Like Simon Says, but with Taco!

The Quiet Game - Try to be silent for as long as you can! Go ahead, try not to giggle!

SSSHHH!

And lastly, what is your favorite song to dance to? Play it and sing along while you practice your favorite dance moves.

You've made it! You are now ready to train your Treindeer! Remember to practice everything in the book so that when you get your Triendeer, you're ready to be the best trainer that you can be! Marshmallow, Taco and Jules will send you notes to your parents' email to help you with training your own Treindeer.

Be sure to ask your parents to check for them. Sometimes the notes will even be from me or Arya. We love to say hello! And with that, we say goodbye for now. Good luck with training!

PARENTS:
Get your little ones' official Treindeer Training Certificate now that they have completed the training. More importantly, have them pick out and name their own very own online Treindeer to train! They will receive emails (sent to you) including personal notes, activities and more to help train their Treindeer. These will provide additional lessons that reinforce all the learnings from this book to engage and educate your child. We also send photos of your Treindeer in the off season, playing in the North Pole and beyond, and even with Santa. Learn more and sign up at Treindeer.com

CPSIA information can be obtained
at www.ICGtesting.com
Printed in the USA
BVHW020014220821
614638BV00030B/69